A Children's Story about Prairie Wildlife

THE HOLE STORY

By Sally Plumb
Illustrated by Ross Burden

Badlands Natural History Association

Author
Sally Plumb

Illustrator
Ross Burden

Project Coordinator
Midge Johnston

BADLANDS NATURAL HISTORY ASSOCIATION

Published by the Badlands Natural History Association

Box 47, Interior, South Dakota 57750

ISBN #0-912410-14-0

THE HOLE STORY

A Park Ranger brought Kit to the Badlands in a box one evening. He was a ferret— and not just any ferret, but a black-footed one at that!

His eyes shone green behind a wide black mask
and his thin body was long and light.
The tip of his tail and his four feet
were as black as the night.

K it's mother had spent her whole life in a zoo,
for there aren't many black-footed ferrets left in the world.
Kit was even more special—
he would go back to the prairie!
His mother taught him the lessons he'd need,
for out in the wild, it's hard to succeed.

His return had been planned from the time he was young,
still white, with no black marks at all.
Now here he was, fully grown, at last,
and the prairie animals watched him carefully.

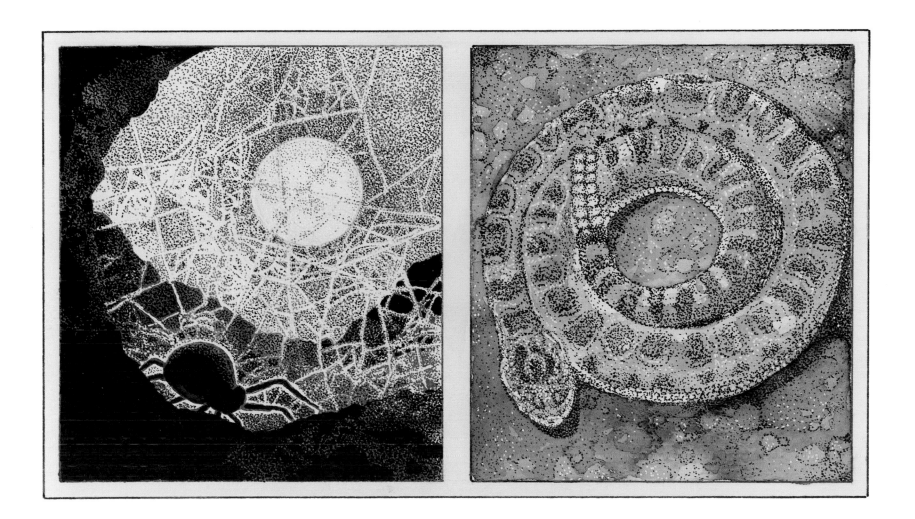

The spider stopped spinning her web,
the snake shook his rattles,
and the great-horned owl gave one long cry.
Digger, king of the prairie dogs, barked in anger.

And Kit?
Kit felt curious and scared.
Noises rustled.
Eyes flickered in the twilight.
The wind moaned from the black holes
of the prairie dog town.

Kit stared at them.
No one made a better hole for a ferret
than a prairie dog!
Kit remembered his mother's lesson:

"Prairie dogs live down holes,
So do mice and also voles,
don't think long about the rest.
Prairie dogs taste the very best!"

Kit's mouth began to water!
Soon, he would leave his cage and...

CLICKETY-CLACK, WELCOME BACK!
CLICKETY-CLACK, WELCOME BACK!
A rattlesnake lifted its head and flicked its tongue.
Its rattles beat out a rhythm:

"The night is waiting, why do you stall?
The prairie dog king waits for you now!
The bigger the Digger, the harder you fall—
The fate that awaits you, waits for us all!"

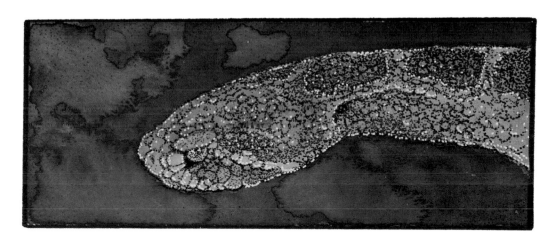 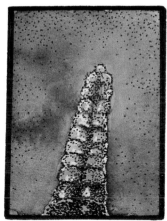

"KKTT...KKTT...KKTT!" Kit squeaked.
The snake circled slyly,
then slid down a burrow without a sound.

Kit stared at the holes again.
A prairie dog, waiting for him?
Many were bigger than he,
with long digging claws and sharp teeth—
but in the zoo, everything had been easy!"
Kit decided that dinner could wait.
He sat quietly all night long,
and did not stir from his cage.

Dawn came at last.
Bison munched, grasshoppers buzzed
and prairie dogs chattered.
Kit wondered which one was Digger
and the breeze suddenly felt cold.

In truth, winter was not faraway.
Soon the prairie dogs would become sleepy and slow, spending long hours in their holes.
Kit would also need a burrow, for the prairie winter was too cold to live above the ground.

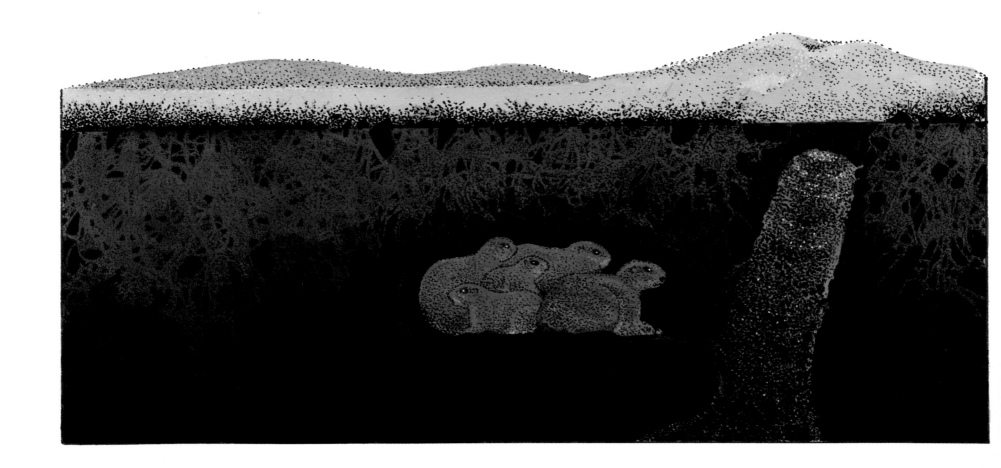

Suddenly, a black widow spider ran across his paw!
Kit hissed, startled.
She waved a leg, showing her red mark.
"Your are not for me, my sweet.
Not for me, your four black feet!
I have a bite, yes, that's true—
But Digger's bite waits for you!"

Creeping lightly away, she disappeared into a hole.
Kit's head sank and he curled up sadly,
one paw across his eyes.

W hen he awoke, the sun was setting.
Kit was tired of his cage and very hungry, indeed!
Taking one keep breath, hedged forward and slipped, finally,
through the small opening and out onto the quiet prairie.

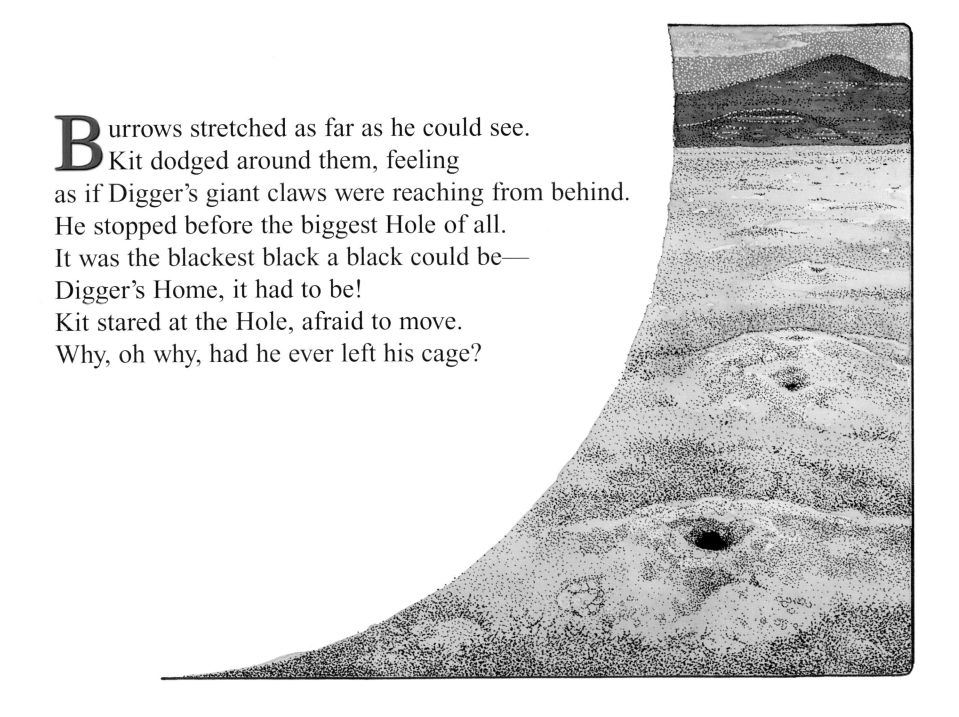

Burrows stretched as far as he could see.
Kit dodged around them, feeling
as if Digger's giant claws were reaching from behind.
He stopped before the biggest Hole of all.
It was the blackest black a black could be—
Digger's Home, it had to be!
Kit stared at the Hole, afraid to move.
Why, oh why, had he ever left his cage?

Far above, a great-horned owl took note.
Hunting tonight, the owl had seen the empty cage
and had circled, searching...
There it was, with its silly black feet!
Staying put so nicely!
"What a treat!
What a feat!
Tonight I'll dine on ferret meat!"

The great-horned owl plunged down!

A shadow passed over Kit
and his heart hammered his mother's lesson:

"Badger, owl, coyote and fox,
   will grab your neck and scratch your socks!
   Keep alert when slinking around!
   If one comes by, get underground!"

K it looked around wildly!
Nowhere to go—
but into the hole, itself!
Shaking from tip to top,
Kit dashed inside!
A long claw ruffled his back
as the owl blocked the
entrance
and the stars went black!

K it fled down the Hole, brushing against its dry sides.
Fine hairs on his paws helped him feel in the dark.
They met nothing except earth.
He stopped, listening hard.
Silence. Though the hole smelled
like prairie dog,
it must be empty, after all.
He was safe!

But Kit could not have been more wrong...
At the end of the tunnel, Digger waited.
Black-footed ferrets meant danger for prairie dogs
and the King of the Mound had not slept that night.
He heard the scatter of soil
and now he was expecting a fight...
The ferret was almost here,
coming quietly on the prowl!
just one more bend and—NOW!

igger shrieked, springing forward
and Kit fell back with a terrified squeak!
The king charged, all nails and teeth,
leaving the ferret with no time to think!

His eyes closed, Kit leapt out blindly,
sinking his claws out and down!
Unfortunately for the king,
the first "thing" they found
was his large behind so soft and round!

Digger squealed and raced up the tunnel. Kit was dragged along after, clutching for dear life! Hold on, Kit, hold on! Reaching a low part, the hurrying king broke loose at last! Before Kit could pick himself up, the air cleared and Digger was gone...

That night the rattlesnake coiled alone,
    the spider feasted on what she had caught,
the owl went hungry,
and Digger found a new hole before dawn.
And Kit?
Kit licked his four black paws and thought:

  "Forget to wander and cease to roam,
    A big, dark hole is the very best home!"
He was back on the prairie to stay.

The End

Black-tailed Prairie Dog
(Cynomys ludovicianus)

Black-tailed prairie dogs are stocky, burrowing ground squirrels and live in holes which are about 15 feet long and 3 to 6 feet deep. Their burrows are marked by mounds of earth, which make excellent lookout perches and can also prevent flooding. Although most active during the day, prairie dogs retreat into their holes to shelter from the the sun, bad weather, or for protection from danger. They live together in "towns", which, in turn, are divided into "coteries". A coterie is usually made up by one adult male, several adult females and any young offspring. They hotly defend this territory and also share play, nuzzling and grooming, even greeting each other by touching their teeth together in a a kiss!

Prairie dogs mate in the spring and females prepare grass-lined nest areas underground. In approximately thirty-four days, the pups are born blind and hairless and must be protected from all dangers until they are six weeks old. At that time, they come above the ground to eat and are quickly weaned. They are nearly full grown by fall and live between three and four years.

Prairie dogs communicate constantly—their common name "dog" comes from the bark-like yip that they use as a warning cry. they eat grasses and forbs and are preyed upon by badgers, weasels, coyotes, hawks, eagles, and of course, the endangered black-footed ferret.

Once very numerous, poisoning, disease and the settling of the Great Plains has reduced the historic range of prairie dogs by 98 percent. Indeed, two of the five species of prairie dogs, the Utah and the Mexican, are now listed as threatened or endangered.

Prairie Rattlesnake
(Crotalus viridis)

After the last frost disappears each spring, a common resident of the plains reappears, the prairie rattlesnake. During the winter, this reptile hibernates in an underground den, often sharing its refuge with hundreds of other snakes.

During warmer months, a rattlesnake returns above ground and eats two to three times its own body weight. The more a snake eats, the faster it grows. With each growth spurt, the snake sheds its old skin and adds a new section of rattles to its tail. Old rattles tend to become worn and break off, however, so the number of rattles is not a accurate way to gauge a snakes age. Prairie rattlesnakes mate in late summer and give birth to a litter of seven to twelve live young in the fall. The newborns are six to twelve inches long and their venom is more concentrated than that of the adults'.

It is well known that this reptile often rattles its tail as a warning of its intention to bite. Less well known is that its poison is produced in venom glands in the snakes cheeks. These glands are connected to two long hollow fangs, which fold up inside the mouth when not in use. When biting, the snake extends its fangs, which fill with venom squeezed from the glands by the reptile's powerful jaw muscles. The poison is delivered to its victim through slits in the front of the fangs. The prairie rattlesnake has poor eyesight, but gathers information with its forked tongue and heat sensitive pits on its face. Usually a night hunter, it feeds on small mammals, birds, and reptiles. Once it bites, it waits for its prey to die, before swallowing it whole-but with a full belly, it is unlikely to escape hungry eagles, owls, and hawks!

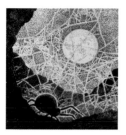

Western Black Widow Spider
(Latrodectus hesperus)

A small male black widow spider, long-legged and marked with four red streaks on the sides of its abdomen, courts the female by plucking the strings of her web. She is larger, glossy black, with the famous red hourglass on her underside. After mating, she may regard her partner as prey and devour him. Afterwards, she will lay between 250-750 eggs in a tan, papery cocoon which hangs from her web and incubates for twenty days. Baby spiders are white with black markings on their abdomen and full growth requires two to three more months. The females live approximately two years and the males, obviously, not as long!

Having no ears and eight eyes with limited vision, black widows survive mainly by their sense of touch. Home webs are built in rock piles, wood piles, abandoned rodent holes and other dark places. Webs are large, messy, and made of very strong silk from the spinnerets at the base of the spider's abdomen. Once a web is completed, the female will hang upside down and rarely leave.

A black widow is not aggressive, waiting quietly for its food: insects, centipedes and other spiders, to come to it. Prey is chewed, soaked with enzymes to predigest it and later sucked into the black widow's stomach. Males do not bite at all and females only bite captured prey or in self-defense. These bites, however, are painful to humans and require a doctor's care.

Great Horned Owl
(Bubo virginianus)

Also called "big-hoot owl", "king owl" and "winged tiger", the great horned is the largest owl in North America and lives up to twenty years in the wild. Females are larger with wing spans between 36 to 60 inches. In appearance, the great horned owl varies in color from light to dark brown, has a white throat and tufts of feathers on its head called "ears" or "horns". This bird lives throughout North America in woodlands, swamps, prairies and deserts.

Great horned owls often pirate hawk, squirrel, heron, and even eagle nests. Breeding in December and laying two to three eggs, the female may then pluck her own breast and stomach feathers in order to put her direct body heat over her eggs. Incubation lasts about one month and the chicks hunt out of their home nests until the following autumn.

Great horned owls are fierce nocturnal hunters and can fly more than forty miles per hour. They prey on just about any small living animal, including mammals, reptiles, insects, frogs, fish and other birds and are able to carry off up to three times their own weight. In cold winter climates, they may store their food, allowing it to freeze. At mealtime, they simply sit on their frozen cache until it thaws and becomes soft enough to eat!

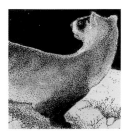

Black-footed Ferret
(Mustela nigripes)

Black-footed ferrets do not have easy lives and survive only three to four years in the wild., Baby "kits" are born plain, with no distinct markings. They are secretive animals that are most active at night. So closely are their lives interwoven with those of prairie dogs, for both food and the shelter of their burrows, that the Lakota Sioux named them "pispiza etopa sapa" or black-masked prairie dog".

Being solitary by nature, adult black-footed ferrets only come together briefly during breeding season, and produce one litter per year with an average of three kits. When the kits are around six weeks old, they learn to hunt. By this time, they have developed their distinctive markings. Yellowish brown fur with a black-tipped tail and four black feet blends into the prairie and bright eyes stare out from a broad lack mask. They are small animals, being only 18-24 inches long (including a 5-6 inch tail) while the prairie dogs they hunt may be twice their size and weight.

To survive, a black-footed ferret must kill approximately 150 prairie dogs every year. Rather than hibernating in the winter, it must emerge from underground every 2 to 6 days to hunt. Effective as it is as a predator, the black-footed ferret is not at the top of the food chain and is preyed upon by coyotes, badgers, owls, foxes and others.

In 1967, due to massive habitat loss, the black-footed ferret was one of the first species to be listed as endangered under the new Endangered Species Act. In 1981, when they were thought extinct, a small group was found near Meeteetse, Wyoming. This group was nearly destroyed due to a fatal disease outbreak, and in 1987, the last surviving eighteen ferrets were taken into captivity to begin a breeding and reintroduction program. Today, enough kits have been born that efforts are underway to reintroduce the back-footed ferret to healthy prairie dog populations in Montana and South Dakota. Although this sites have met with initial success, an uncertain story remains to be told before we know if the black-footed ferret has returned to the prairies to stay.

About the Author

Sally Plumb grew up near Evergreen, Colorado on her great-grandfather's Rocky Mountain homestead. She spent summers in the Teton, Gros Ventre and Absaroka mountains of Wyoming, living in the isolated field camps of her geologist father. During college, Sally worked as a seasonal wilderness guard in Bighorn National Forest, Wyoming. It was here that she met her future husband, Glenn. Their lengthy courtship endured prolonged separations as Sally entered graduate school in Environmental Interpretation and Glenn lived in the Wyoming Red Desert studying wild horse ecology. After marriage, they managed a Nature Conservancy Prairie Preserve in South Dakota and a research station in Grand Teton National Park, Wyoming. The reintroduction of North America's most endangered land mammal, the black-footed ferret, brought them to Badlands National Park, South Dakota, where Glenn served as the park's wildlife biologist. Home is currently Yellowstone National Park, Wyoming. Sally currently works as a seasonal interpretive park ranger and also on the park's ongoing oral history project. She continues to enjoy the wonder of nature with her family through work, art and play.